HPS 1482

HARRISON BIRTWISTLE

OBOE QUARTET

FOR OBOE, VIOLIN, VIOLA AND CELLO

Boosey & Hawkes Music Publishers Ltd
www.boosey.com

Published by Boosey & Hawkes Music Publishers Ltd
Aldwych House
71–91 Aldwych
London
WC2B 4HN

www.boosey.com

© Copyright 2011 by Boosey & Hawkes Music Publishers Ltd

ISMN 979-0-060-12498-3
ISBN 978-0-85162-835-6
HPS 1482

First impression 2013

Printed in England by The Halstan Printing Group, Amersham, Bucks

Music origination by Simon Smith and The Note Factory

Movement 1 was commissioned by
LUCERNE FESTIVAL for the Swiss oboist,
conductor and composer Heinz Holliger

It was first performed in Lucerne as part of
LUCERNE FESTIVAL, Sommer 2009 on 15 September 2009

Movement 2 was commissioned by WDR

Movements 3 and 4 were commissioned by
the Nash Ensemble with funds provided by
the Ernst von Siemens Musikstiftung

First performance: 24 March 2010
at the Wigmore Hall, London

The world premiere of the complete work was given on 8 May 2011
at Wittener Tage für neue Kammermusik

Duration: 18 minutes

Set of parts available on sale
(ISMN 979-0-060-12605-5)

Note on symbols

Forked arrows indicate approximate place of entry. A right-angled arrow indicates tempo independent of the main beat and other instruments.

⋀ = short pause

🎵 = stressed, very slightly detached

Accidentals apply for a full bar. In free, unbarred passages, they are given for each affected note, except for immediately repeated pitches.

OBOE QUARTET

HARRISON BIRTWISTLE

I

19025

2

Ob and Vl not synchronised

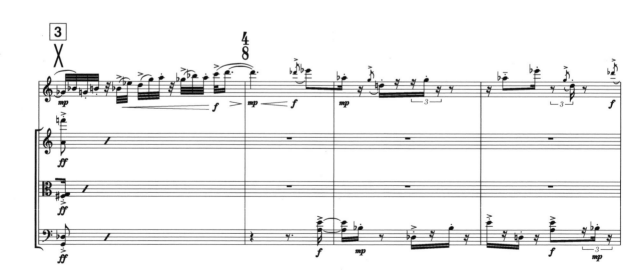

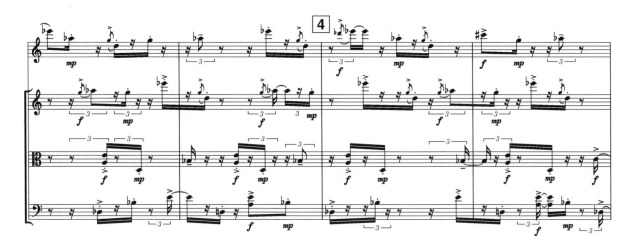

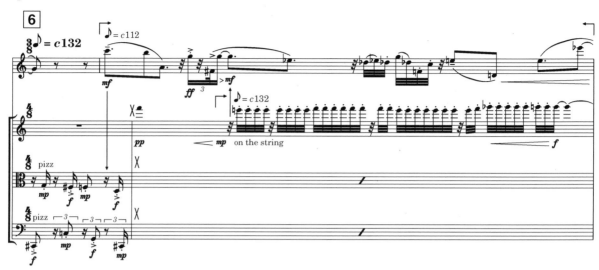

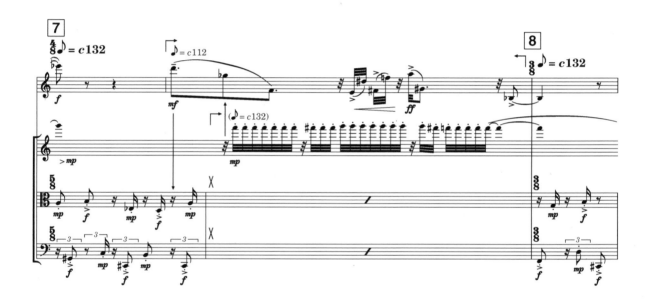

rall _ _ _ _ _ _ _ _ _ _ _ _ _ _ ♪ = *c*72

★ Oboe's grace notes, up to fig 13, sound *on* the beat.

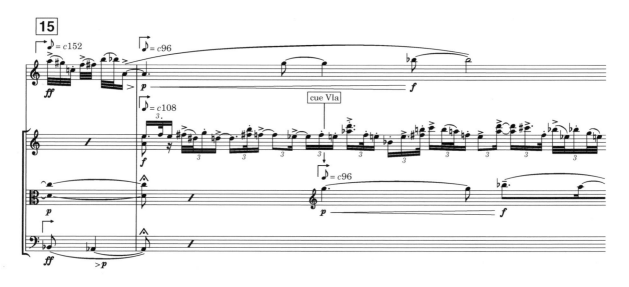

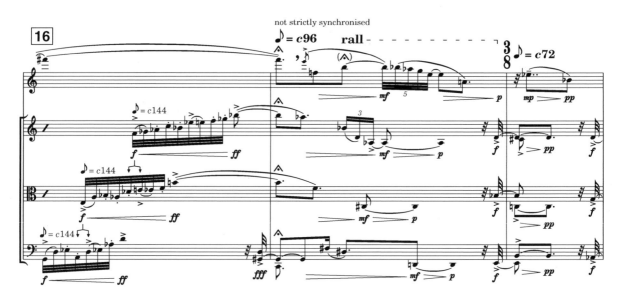

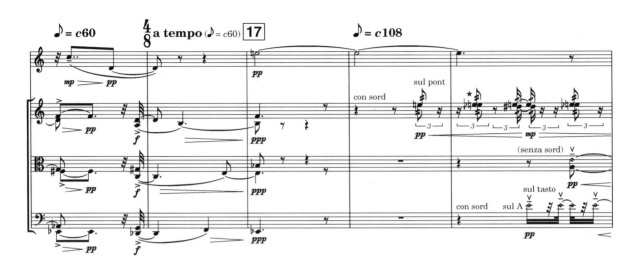

★♭ = quarter-tone flat

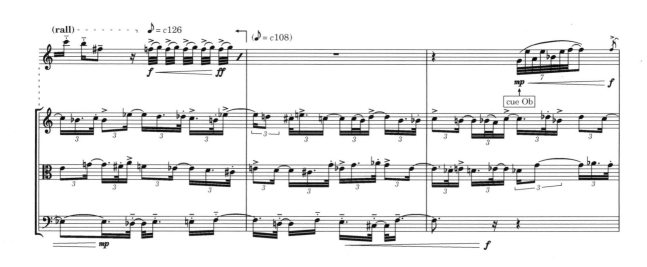

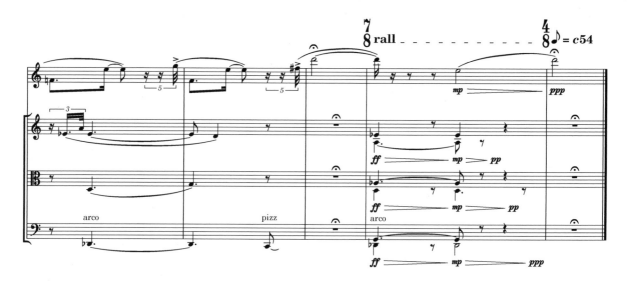

II

19256

14

19256

III

19131

IV

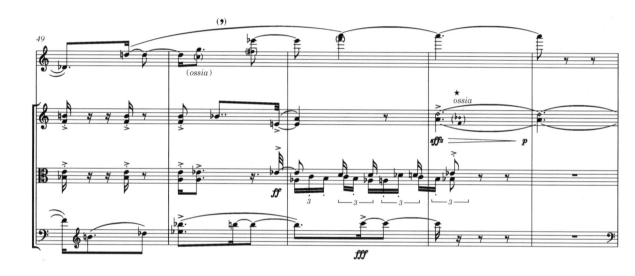

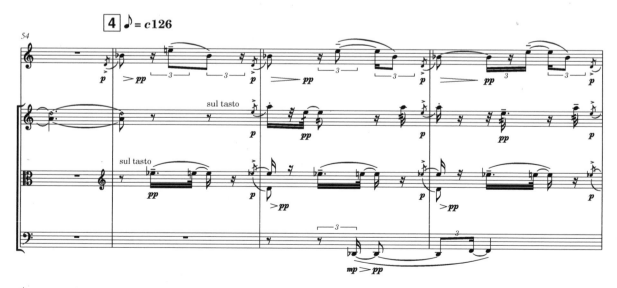

★ *ossia* applies only if Oboe plays an F

★1) ♩♩ means ♩.♪ ♪

★2) In this passage all notes marked ⪦ should be in clear relief